writing guides

ACTIVITIES

Recounts

HILARY BRAUND & DEBORAH GIBBON

NON-FICTION

FOR AGES

5-7

CONTENTS

INTRODUCTION

The Scholastic *Writing Guides* series provides teachers with ideas and projects that promote a range of writing, bringing insights from educational research into the classroom. Each guide explores a different type of writing and provides example material, background information, photocopiable activities and teaching suggestions. Their aim is to enable teachers to guide the writing process, share planning ideas and develop themes as a context for writing activities.

The materials:
- motivate children with interesting activities
- break complex types of writing into manageable teaching units
- focus on and develop the typical features of particular types of writing
- provide original approaches to teaching.

Each book is divided into sections, beginning with examples of the type of writing being taught. These are followed by ideas for developing writing and projects that will extend over a series of sessions.

SECTION ONE: USING GOOD EXAMPLES

Section One looks at good examples of the genre, with the emphasis on using texts to stimulate and develop writing. Two example texts are shared, and questions that focus the discussion on their significant features are suggested. This is followed by activities that explore what the texts can teach us about writing, enabling teachers to compare the two texts and to go on to model the type of writing presented in the guide.

SECTION TWO: DEVELOPING WRITING

Section Two moves from reading to writing. This section provides activities that prompt and support children in planning and writing. A range of approaches includes planning templates and strategies to stimulate ideas. The activities refine children's ideas about the type of writing being developed and give them focused writing practice in the context of scaffolded tasks. Teacher's notes support each activity by explaining the objective and giving guidance on delivery.

SECTION THREE: WRITING

Section Three moves on to writing projects. Building upon the earlier work in Section Two, these projects aim to develop the quality of writing and provide a selection of ideas for class or group work on a particular theme or idea. The teacher may choose to use some or all of the ideas presented in each project as a way of weaving the strategies developed in Section Two into a more complex and extended writing task.

SECTION FOUR: REVIEW

Section Four supports the assessment process. Children are encouraged to reflect on the type of writing they are tackling and to evaluate how effectively their work has met the criteria for the genre identified in Section One.

What Can I Write?

Rosie's teacher has asked her to write about what she did in the holidays. Here are just two pages from her finished writing.

On Saturday we went to a big store to look for a new dress for Mum. She was going to a special party. There were rows and rows of dresses. I looked at all of them. Then when I looked for Mum I couldn't find her. It was scary. I almost cried. A girl from the shop asked if I was lost. I told her my name and she went and spoke into a microphone. You could hear her all over the place.

She said, "Will Mrs Lee please come to the Manager's office where your daughter Rosie is waiting?"

I was so pleased to see Mum, but she looked cross and told me never to wander off like that again!

Mum's friend Paula and her baby George came round at lunch time. George is really nice. I call him Chubbychops. I told Paula it was a pity we didn't have any biscuits for George.

Paula said, "Don't worry, Rosie. You can give him his cauliflower cheese for lunch."

Just as I gave him a ginormous spoonful, he sneezed! It went all over me.

Mum and Paula laughed, then George laughed.

I didn't think it was funny.

Korky Paul: Biography of an Illustrator

Where was he born?

Korky was born in Africa. He was born on 5th December in 1951. He has four sisters and two brothers. He grew up in a small village in Zimbabwe.

Korky's parents are called Barbara and Denzil. His mum was a nurse. His dad did lots of different jobs. His favourite job was drilling for water.

Where did he go to school?

Korky went to Godfrey Huggins Junior School in Zimbabwe. He then went to Estcourt High School in South Africa. His favourite subjects were history and art. He started to draw when he was five years old.

Korky spent a lot of time drawing. He drew on his pencil boxes and all over his exercise books. When he was a teenager, he drew posters for school dances.

Recounts are often the first genre of structured non-fiction writing that children experience. Young children will often write about events in their own lives, starting with very simple recollections of things they have done (in 'news', for example). In school, we often concentrate more on developing narrative and poetic structures; but while we all know how to write about events that have happened, there is often less understanding of the language related to the genre of recounts, and consequently of how to develop and extend children's writing in this respect.

Recounts retell events, and this style of writing is used for biographies, reports and historical information. They are usually written in the past tense, with events recalled in chronological order, focusing on a person or people and the actions they have performed.

The structure of recounts can be broken down into three sections: the orientation, where we are told where, when and who the recount is about; the events recall what happened, and finally the ending provides a reorientation.

Shared activities

Text extracts

The extracts on pages 4 and 5 give two different examples of recounts. The first, from Martina Selway's *What Can I Write? Rosie Writes Again* (Red Fox), is a style of writing that may be familiar to the children – it is written as though by a child who is writing 'news' at school. The second is an example of biographical writing, telling us a little about the childhood of an illustrator the children may know of: Korky Paul. It is taken from *Korky Paul: Biography of an Illustrator* (Heinemann).

These two extracts are intended to be enlarged and displayed for shared reading as a group or class. When first reading the extracts, talk about the purpose of the writing. Introduce the three sections of a recount by asking the children to recall who the recount is about and the key events. Pages 8 and 9 contain two activities that can be used as follow-up group or class activities in conjunction with the extracts.

What's it all about?

This activity aims to help children recognise the overall structure of recounts and to extract information from the texts. Explain to the children that recounts have an opening (orientation) that gives information on who the recount is about and when and where it is set; one or more events, and a clear ending (reorientation). Using an enlarged copy of photocopiable page 8, look with the children at the structure of the first page of Rosie's writing. Part of the factfile is already completed to model the kind of information that is required; work with the children to complete the framework and then go on to complete the whole of the blank framework below, using information from the second page of Rosie's writing.

All about...

This activity looks specifically at biographical writing. Using the biography on page 5 as a model, encourage the children to identify the relevant information from the extract that is used to answer the questions on photocopiable page 9. Then, as a class, use an enlarged copy of the questions underneath to work together to create a biographical piece of writing about an invited adult volunteer (a parent, classroom assistant or office manager, for example). Use the headings to plan with the children the questions they should ask, then conduct a 'press conference' style interview, with the children asking questions as you make notes on the board. Work with the children to turn these notes into a biography of the volunteer.

Taking ideas further

The opening two sets of extracts and accompanying activities have introduced the topic of Recounts to the children and begun to draw attention to particular features of the genre. The extracts from *What Can I Write? Rosie Writes Again* provide examples of a personal recount, and will hopefully have helped children to see that their own everyday experiences are worth writing about and can be made interesting to read. While being part of a much longer recount, each extract stands alone and sets an example of the structure of a recount written in the first person, with much use of the pronoun 'I'. The extract from the biography of Korky Paul provides an example of a recount written in the third person, and instead of retelling a particular incident it gives information about aspects of Korky Paul's life.

The difference between writing in the first and third person can be highlighted further by looking at the difference between biographical and autobiographical writing with the children.

You and me

The activity on page 10 compares the two extracts in terms of style and their use of the first and third person. Display an enlarged copy of photocopiable page 10 and, working with either the whole class or groups of children, fill in the gaps in the two extracts using the correct words. As you work through the extracts, discuss the purpose of each of these recounts with the children – were they written to provide accurate information or to be an entertaining 'story' for the reader? Talk about the similarities of the two extracts – that they both tell us about events in a person's life – and the differences in terms of who may have written each – Rosie writing about herself, while another author writes about Korky Paul.

Recounts

The poster on photocopiable page 11 can be enlarged and used as an aid to promote discussion about what the children have found out so far about recounts, including their purpose in providing information about events that have happened and whether the author is writing about themselves or someone else. Examples of recounts are given in a range of formats to show how the genre can be used for writing in everyday life. You might want to make a collection of examples of other kinds of recounts from real life to read to the children and display along with the poster. These could include local and national newspaper reports, simple biographies of famous people and appropriate letters that retell events that have happened to another person. Collections of books that include recounts in different formats can also be displayed, including 'stories' from history (for example, that of Guy Fawkes, or the first Lunar landing) and writing in diary formats (Samuel Pepys' diary, for example).

Extension ideas

Using this collection of recounts, discuss with the children the purpose of each. For example, historical recounts are written to provide information for the reader, diaries are for personal writing, and biographical writing is often written to entertain. Encourage the children to identify the 'who', 'when', 'where' and 'what' of each recount – this could be done as a class or group activity as you read examples from the collection out loud, or you could set up an interactive display where the children are invited to read the examples for themselves and fill in a chart to identify the four aspects of the recount themselves.

What's it all about?

OPENING

Who: Mum and Rosie.   **Where:** At a big store.

What: _____   **When:** _____

EVENTS

● Rosie couldn't find Mum in the shop.

● _____

● _____

● Mum came to find Rosie.

ENDING

_____

OPENING

Who: _____   **Where:** _____

What: _____   **When:** _____

EVENTS

● _____

● _____

● _____

● _____

ENDING

_____

All about...

Where was Korky born?
Korky was born in Africa in a country called Zimbabwe.

What are Korky's parents called?
His mum is called Barbara and his dad is called Denzil.

How many brothers and sisters does Korky have?
He has four sisters and two brothers.

When was he born?
He was born on December 5th 1951.

What did Korky spend a lot of time doing?
He spent a lot of time drawing.

What were Korky's favourite subjects at school?
He liked history and art.

What school did he go to?
Korky went to Godfrey Huggins Junior School and Estcourt High School.

Where was _____ born?

How many brothers and sisters does _____ have?

What were _____ favourite subjects at school?

What did _____ spend a lot of time doing?

When was _____ born?

What are _____ parents called?

What school did _____ go to?

writing guides: **RECOUNTS**

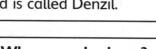

You and me

When you write about yourself you use words such as **I, me** and **we**. When you write about someone else you use words such as **he, she, his** or **her**. Can you add the correct words that have been removed from these two extracts?

On Saturday _____ went to a big store to look for a new dress for Mum. _____ was going to a special party. There were rows and rows of dresses. _____ looked at all of them. Then when _____ looked for Mum _____ couldn't find _____. It was scary. _____ almost cried. A girl from the shop asked if _____ was lost. _____ told _____ my name and _____ went and spoke into a microphone. You could hear _____ all over the place.

Korky was born in Africa. _____ was born on 5th December in 1951. _____ has four sisters and two brothers. _____ grew up in a small village in Zimbabwe. Korky's parents are called Barbara and Denzil. _____ mum was a nurse. _____ dad did lots of different jobs. _____ favourite job was drilling for water.

---

writing guides: **RECOUNTS**

Recounts

What is a recount?
A recount tells the reader about events that have already happened.

Who: Bella and myself
When: Sunday
Where: At the park
What: Playing on the swings and having an ice-cream

Harwood Primary School End of Year Report

Sammy worked hard this year. She found maths a struggle early on but since Easter she has made excellent progress. She enjoyed writing and book making. She learned how to kick and throw a ball in P.E.

First we went on the swings.

Next we bought an ice-cream

It was fun.

On Sunday I went to the park with Bella.

Who: Sammy
When: This year
Where: At school
What: Sammy's learning

Daily News   15p

CARNIVAL CAPERS!

Saturday afternoon was carnival time in the town centre. The crowds were entertained by stilt walkers, clowns and jugglers. A big costume parade took place at 2 o'clock, and then the carnival finished with a fantastic firework display.

Who: Danny
When: Yesterday
Where: At the seaside
What: Going to the funfair and riding on the big wheel

Who: Carnival-goers
When: Saturday
Where: Town centre
What: Carnival entertainment, costume parade and firework display

BLACKPOOL

Dear Manjot,
It has been very sunny at the seaside. Yesterday I went to the fun-fair. I had a go on the big wheel. I thought it was very exciting. Danny

Manjot
3 Prince St.
Hackney
LONDON

writing guides: **RECOUNTS**

SECTION TWO

DEVELOPING WRITING

The photocopiable activities in this section develop aspects of the recount genre more specifically. The importance of the sequence of events is revisited several times. Giving the children the chance to write recounts about themselves, and about (or in role as) other people or imagined characters they know, develops the use of pronouns and the difference between writing in the first and third person. The vocabulary of recounts is modelled through the use of writing frames and simple note-making is encouraged in the development of biographical writing. The overall structure of recounts, and the use of detail and description to add interest, is focused on in both oral and written activities.

Modelling

There are lots of opportunities for modelling the writing of recounts in the course of a school day: plenary sessions for any kind of work; reviewing work undertaken over a week or a half-term; recapping on work covered during the day or recalling special events in school. Use these opportunities for regular shared writing practice. As well as focusing on the structure of recounts in such situations, try to encourage the development of a wide vocabulary, particularly the use of conjunctions, and spelling and grammar rules appropriate to the age and ability of your class.

Activities should be modelled for the whole class or smaller groups before the children are asked to work on them independently. Many can be completed as a shared activity to allow less confident readers and writers to participate.

Making notes

Other, more extended and specifically planned, shared writing activities could focus on the modelling of note-making to inform later recount writing. You could make notes on the board while children orally retell events from their own lives; these notes can then be used by the children to structure a more extended piece of recount writing.

A range of writing frames can also be developed to serve different purposes, such as recounting a class trip, recording how an activity or investigation was carried out, or reviewing a completed topic.

Any work on particular aspects of writing recounts and the planning activities should be kept so it can later be used by the children to support their independent writing of complete recounts.

In order

For less-experienced writers, visual prompts could be used to help develop the skills needed for successful recounts, particularly the importance of sequencing events. These visual prompts can then form the basis of oral recounts, simple written recounts or for the children to develop their own pictorial version of events. For example, pictures and symbols to represent the common events of the school day can be made, laminated and re-used regularly with the class to recall the order of the activities of the day.

MY DAY AT SCHOOL

WHAT YOU NEED

Copies of photocopiable page 16 and board or flip chart .

WHAT TO DO

Ask the children to tell you about the events they can think of that happen during an average day at school. As they tell you about events use careful questioning to encourage them to use vocabulary related to time, for example: *When do you have quiet reading? Do you go out to play before you have your lunch?* In the course of the discussion write down key vocabulary related to the events of the day, for example 'assembly', 'playtime' on the board.

Give out copies of photocopiable page 16. Help the children to read through the sentence starters before asking them to complete the worksheet, filling in their own information in the spaces.

OBJECTIVE
■ To develop a sense of chronology when writing recounts about events in their own lives.

READ ALL ABOUT IT!

WHAT YOU NEED

Copies of photocopiable page 17, examples of newspaper reports.

WHAT TO DO

Give out copies of photocopiable page 17, and look at the newspaper report at the top of the page with the children. Ask them if they know what type of writing the page represents. Show some other real-life examples of newspaper reports and discuss the features that are used – headlines, writing in columns, pictures with captions and so on. Read through the story of Thimble the lost dog with the children, as told in the report.

Now tell the children that they are going to have a go at writing a recount in the style of a newspaper report about a lost cat. The photocopiable page gives some ideas for the structure and sentence starters, but they should be encouraged to use original ideas if they can, rather than simply replicating the details of the 'lost dog' story. As a finishing touch, they can add a picture in the space provided.

OBJECTIVE
■ To structure a recount in the form of a newspaper report.

A STORY IN PICTURES

WHAT YOU NEED

Copies of photocopiable page 18, scissors, glue, paper, writing materials.

WHAT TO DO

Give out copies of photocopiable page 18 and ask the children to describe what is happening in each of the pictures – does it make sense? Explain that the pictures are not in the correct order and that they should cut them out, arrange them in the correct sequence and stick them down on another sheet of paper.

When they have done this, ask them to imagine that they are either a reporter from the newspaper or one of the children in the pictures, and that they are going to retell the story. How will their recounts differ? Explain in simple terms the differences between a first and third person recount, highlighting the different pronouns used. Ask the children to choose one of the two characters and to write a recount of the story from their perspective, either as individual sentences accompanying each picture or to structure their writing to resemble either a newspaper report or a diary entry.

OBJECTIVES
■ To use visual cues to sequence the events in a recount.
■ To write a recount in either the first or third person.

BIOGRAPHY
WHAT YOU NEED

Copies of photocopiable page 19, paper, writing materials.

WHAT TO DO

Before this activity, you will need to ask around to find out which members of staff are willing and available to be interviewed by the children, and warn them of when this activity is happening!

Ask the children to work in pairs. Give each pair a copy of photocopiable page 19, and tell them that they are going to find an adult in school who is willing and available to be interviewed. Before they set off, read through the questions on the photocopiable page and ask the children if they can think of any further questions that they would like to ask. Explain that as they conduct the interview, they should make notes of the answers given. Encourage them to think about how they will organise the interview – will they both make notes or will only one person write?

Having completed the interview, the children should use the notes they have made to write a short biography of their chosen adult They may like to complete this writing individually or continue to work in pairs. Refer back to the extract from the biography of Korky Paul (page 5) to help the children with the style and format of their writing.

MAKE IT INTERESTING
WHAT YOU NEED

An enlarged copy of photocopiable page 20, paper, writing materials.

WHAT TO DO

Write the following two passages on the board to share with the children:

Yesterday I was at the shops. A man fell over and an ambulance took him to hospital.

Yesterday, which was Tuesday, I went to the corner shop to buy some crisps. As I came out of the shop I saw an old man walking along the pavement. In front of him was a broken paving stone but he didn't see it and tripped over. He really looked like he had hurt himself. A kind lady called for an ambulance. It came really quickly. The man was taken in the ambulance to hospital.

Read both the passages with the children, and discuss the similarities and differences between the two. Ask which was the most interesting to listen to and briefly discuss how detail can bring a story to life. Show the children the enlarged copy of photocopiable page 20. Together, fill in the boxes at the top of the page using information from the recounts written on the board. Discuss with the children the main points of information included in the top half of the box and encourage them to identify additional details which can be added below, for example:

Who: main points – man, added details – old man; Where: main points – shops, added details – the corner shop.

Read the simple recount about Ewan given on the bottom half of the sheet. Ask the children to comment on how it is written. The question below asks the children to add details to make the recount more interesting; ask them what else they would like to know about Ewan and his swimming race. Use the given questions as prompts and add any additional questions that the children think of. Provide the children with paper on which to write their own, more interesting version of 'Ewan's Race'. Explain that they should use their imagination to add extra details, using the questions as prompts for ideas.

ANOTHER POINT OF VIEW
WHAT YOU NEED
Copies of photocopiable page 21, plus an enlarged copy for display; an enlarged copy of photocopiable page 4.

WHAT TO DO
Display enlarged copies of the two extracts. Explain to the children that the passage on photocopiable page 21 is a story about Rosie, the little girl whose writing they looked at earlier. Read through the passage with the children, then compare it with the passage on page 4 and point out the difference – the extract on page 4 was written by Rosie, while the passage on page 21 is just about Rosie. Re-read the passage on page 21 to ensure the children are familiar with the events, then ask them to turn to the person next to them and retell orally what happened to Rosie on Tuesday.

When they have finished, explain to the children that they are now going to rewrite the events of the day as though they were one of the characters – Rosie, Mum or Roland. Give out copies of photocopiable page 21. Encourage the children to refer back to the written passage only if they need a reminder of what happened. On the board, make three columns headed 'Rosie', 'Mum' and 'Roland'. With the children, make a list of prompts for each character outlining what happened to them that day, for example: *Roland: went to Rosie's, played with Gameboy, had a fight, got shouted at, went home.* Ask them to write a full recount of the events of the day from the point of view of their chosen character, using the prompts and original text to help them. Remind them that they will be writing 'in role' as either Mum, Rosie or Roland, and so will be using words such as 'I', 'me' and 'we' in their writing.

OBJECTIVE
■ To understand that people can have different points of view when recounting the same event.

WHO? WHERE? WHAT?
WHAT YOU NEED
An enlarged copy of photocopiable page 22 cut into individual cards, board or flip chart, paper, writing materials.

WHAT TO DO
Display the cards cut from the enlarged copy of page 22, and ask the children to select one from each of the 'who' and 'where' rows, and three verbs from the 'what' section. Write these on the board. Explain to the children that they are going to imagine an event that includes the character, place and actions they have chosen. Work together to construct a written recount of the event on the board, taking suggestions from the children. Having completed an example together, ask the children to work independently, making their own choice of who, what and where from the photocopiable page and writing their own recounts of imagined events.

OBJECTIVE
■ To identify the orientation, subject and actions within a recount.

My day at school

Use this writing frame to write a recount of your day at school. You may want to use these sentence beginnings in your own writing.

Beginning

 To make sure I am ready in time for school I get up at

_____

Events

  Before I go to school I _____

After I have left my house _____

  I arrive at school at _____

During the morning I _____

  After lunch I spend my time _____

At the end of the school day _____

_____

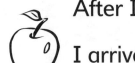 ## Ending

When I am back home I _____

_____

writing guides: **RECOUNTS**

Read all about it!

This is a newspaper report about a lost dog. Read it, then make up your own story about an abandoned cat. Some sentences have been started for you. Remember to add a headline!

NEW HOPE FOR ABANDONED DOG

Last week, Thimble, a small brown dog, was found all alone on some waste ground. He was found by Jade Dennis, who was playing in a nearby playground with some friends. She took the dog to the local police station. The police handed him over to the local dogs' home. Very soon he was spotted by a family who were looking for a new pet.

Thimble now lives happily with Mr and Mrs Samwell and their three children. He is taken for walks every day and enjoys playing with his ball in the

park. As you can see from this picture, Thimble's story has a happy ending!

Last week,

She was found

The cat was taken

Very soon

The cat now

As you can see

A story in pictures

Cut out these pictures and put them in order to show what you think happened. Write a recount either as a newspaper story by a reporter, or as a diary entry for one of the children, telling the story of what happened.

writing guides: **RECOUNTS**

Biography

Find an adult in school to interview about their life, using the questions below. You may be able to think of more questions to ask. Make some notes about what they tell you. Then use your notes to write a short biography of the person you interviewed.

Questions

What do you do?		Where were you born?

Where did you go to school?

What did you do when you left school?		Who's in your family?

Notes

Make it interesting

WHO	
Main points	I, man
Additional details	

WHERE	
Main points	shops
Additional details	

WHEN	
Main points	yesterday
Additional details	

WHAT	
Main points	fell over, ambulance took him to hospital
Additional details	

This is to certify

One day Ewan went swimming. He had a race. He got a certificate.

What things would you like to know? Can you add details to make this recount about Ewan more interesting?

How far did he have to swim?

How old is Ewan?

Which day?

How many children were in the race?

What did the certificate say?

Did he win the race?

What did he do with the certificate?

writing guides: **RECOUNTS**

Another point of view

What happened to Rosie on Tuesday

On Tuesday Rosie wanted to go to the Toy Museum, but she and her Mum had to wait for the TV to be mended.

Roland came round. Rosie got her toys out, but Roland only wanted to play with his Game Boy. He wouldn't let her have a go. They had a fight and Rosie was told off for knocking the vase of flowers over.

Rosie shouted at Roland and Mum yelled at them both to stop squabbling. She told them to play nicely while she made tea.

Roland didn't stay for tea. He wanted to go home. Rosie was glad.

At bedtime Mum said she'd be working tomorrow, and Rosie would have to go to Roland's!

(Based on an extract from *Rosie Writes Again*)

Can you rewrite this account from Rosie, Mum or Roland's point of view?

_____

_____

_____

_____

_____

_____

_____

Who? Where? What?

Who		
Child	Woman	Man

Where		
Shops	Park	School

What		
Writing	Playing	Running
Looking	Sliding	Swinging
Carrying	Buying	Eating
Singing	Choosing	Pushing

writing guides: **RECOUNTS**

Having completed the shared activities based around the initial text extracts in Section One and the individual activities of Section Two, the children should now have a clear understanding of the purpose and structure of recounts. They should be aware that:

- *recounts retell events that have already happened*
- *they retell events in the order that they happened*
- *that they use pronouns consistently*
- *that vocabulary related to the time and sequence of events is important*
- *recounts tell us about the 'who', 'where', 'when' and 'what' of incidents*
- *that detail beyond the basic facts creates interest for the reader.*

The children should now be encouraged to write complete recounts on their own. It is best to begin with recounts of activities that are of personal interest to the children, as this provides them with content that is familiar and already structured in chronological order in their own memories. They can then move on to writing about events further removed from their own experience, which may include: events that have happened within the class or school; events that have happened to other people known to them but which they did not experience personally; or events that they have learned about that happened to people unknown to them or in the distant past. This section encourages and supports children in writing their own recounts.

Who? What? Where? When?

This double-page poster on pages 24–5 provides visual prompts for children, highlighting the 'who', 'where', 'when' (orientation) and 'what' (events) aspects of a recount. Display the poster (or give it to groups of children) as you carry out work on writing recounts. By presenting the prompts in speech bubbles, children are encouraged to see the connection between oral and written recounts recognising how recounts are often written versions of stories they may tell their friends, recalling events that have happened. Vocabulary related to each of the aspects is provided – when working with the class or a group on a particular recount additional appropriate vocabulary could be added.

Writing recounts

The poster on pages 26–7 draws attention to the different ways in which recounts can be written. Again, it can be used either with the whole class or with smaller groups when working on writing recounts. Prompts on the poster encourage the children to think about the style or tone of their work, the purpose of their writing, the format that is most appropriate to the purpose and the range of content. There are also ideas for subjects that can form the basis of recounts, which you may like to use as group activities with the class when practising writing recounts over the course of a half-term. Encourage the children to use the prompts on the poster and to think about different ways of writing their recount when working on the activities.

Presenting work

Pages 28–9 provide ideas for presenting finished work. Unlike when writing fiction, we often find it difficult to present non-fiction work imaginatively and creatively – the suggestions on the poster may help to inspire young writers. Remind the children that recounts are written to entertain as well as providing information, and so the presentation of work should aim to draw the interest of the reader. The ideas suggested on the poster can be used for the presentation of final drafts or as starting points to inspire the initial writing. Display the poster and discuss the suggestions with the children. Pick ideas to work on with the class as appropriate.

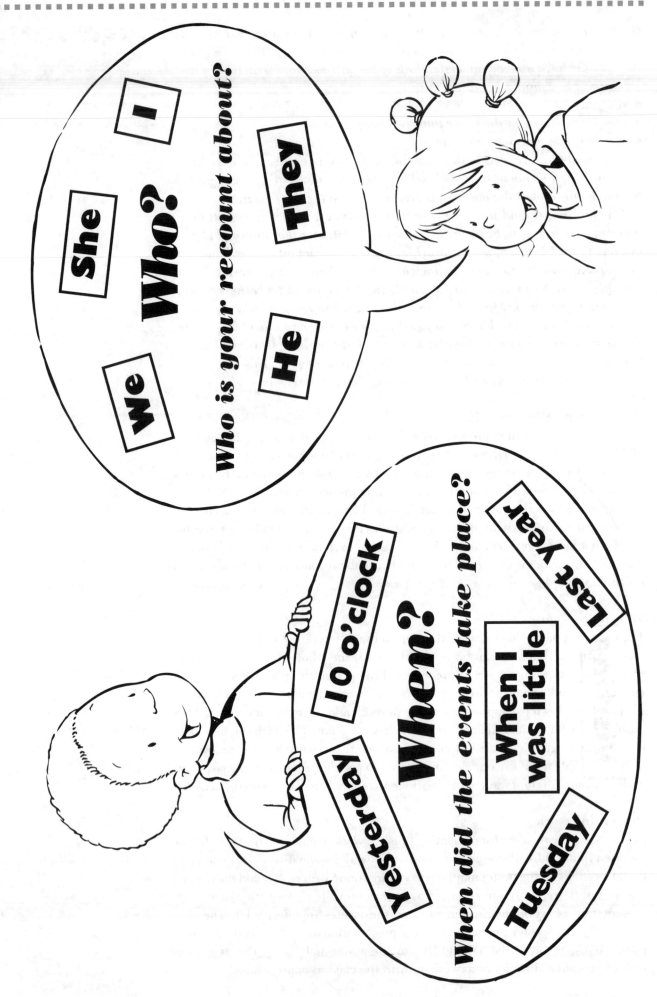

Who is your recount about?

Who?

She
I
We
They
He

When did the events take place?

When?

10 o'clock
Last year
When I was little
Yesterday
Tuesday

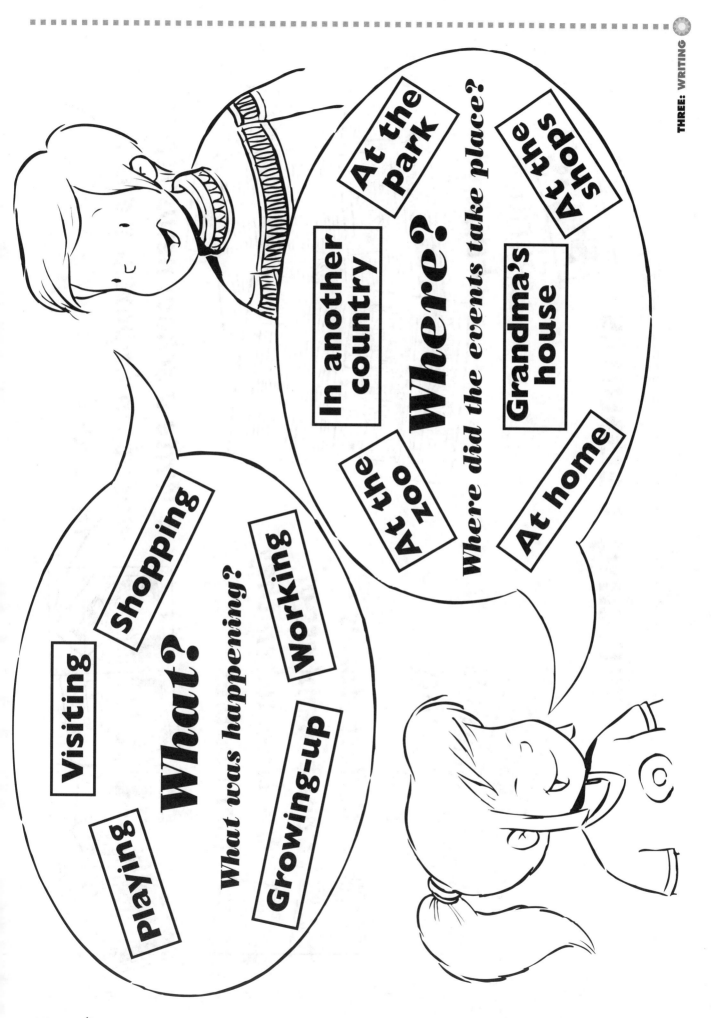

Writing recounts

Style

Serious

Funny

Purpose

Entertaining

Informing

- Collect stories about members of the class when they were babies

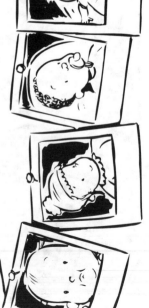

- Write a school newspaper about an important event in school

• Write a letter to a child in another country describing your school day

Format
Letter
Newspaper
Newspaper book
Information

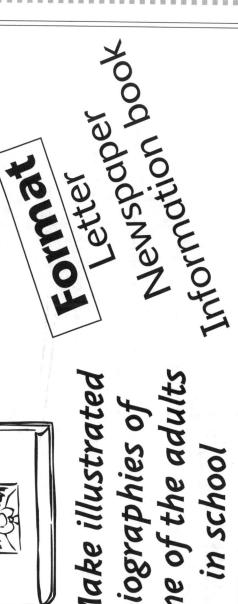

THE AUTOBIOGRAPHY OF A SCHOOL CARETAKER

• Make illustrated biographies of some of the adults in school

• Write a review of your half-term's work, showing all the new things you have learned

REPORT

GEOGRAPHY
P.E.
MATHS
ART
ENGLISH
SCIENCE

Content
Biography
Autobiography
Personal event

Presenting work

Interactive display board

TELL THE CLASS ABOUT INTERESTING EVENTS THAT HAVE HAPPENED TO YOU OUT OF SCHOOL...

EMILY MEETS TV CHEF

CANOE COURSE

NADIM SCOOPS ART PRIZE

SWIMMING 50m

Class book

OUR CLASS BOOK OF FUNNY BABY TALES

Sequence board for the day's activities

first thing in the morning   before dinner   after dinner   before we go home

School newspaper

Recollection of a trip

Shaped zigzag book

Children's work can be reviewed in different ways. Some aspects of the review, including the use of 'writing partners' and discussions with individual children around the points outlined in the 'teacher assessment' section should take place after an initial draft has been produced, and the outcomes of these discussions can then feed into the finished product. There is also a need to assess the finished writing. All assessment and review activities should refer back to the earlier work in Sections One and Two where generic features of the Recounts genre were identified and explored. It is important to remember to assess and review the children's writing in terms of its use of these features rather than simply as a piece of non-fiction writing in general.

Children's self review

Encourage the use of 'writing partners' in helping children to review and develop their drafting skills. By reading their work in progress to a friend, children can build an awareness of how their recount engages the listener, and also take the opportunity to share ideas. They should focus on how a recount enables the reader (or listener) to understand when and where an event happened, who was involved and the order in which the events took place. Children should be reminded that their comments to each other should be supportive rather than negative.

The photocopiable review sheets on pages 31 and 32 can be used with the children in evaluating their finished product. Having worked over an extended period of time, these can help the children to recall the main features of recount writing and to evaluate how successful they have been at using them in their own writing. Alternatively it can be used with children to review their first draft and provide opportunities to make notes of additional aspects to be included in their final version.

Teacher assessment

In assessing the children's work you may like to focus on the following points:
- Does the opening tell us about the setting and who the recount is about?
- Are all the events mentioned in the right order?
- Is vocabulary relating to the passing of time used correctly?
- Is it written consistently in the past tense?
- Is vocabulary used appropriately to add details and interest?

These prompts can be used both when reviewing work in progress with children, and also when accessing finished pieces of writing.

Writing review 1

My recount is about:

_____

At the beginning of my recount the reader finds out:

✔

Details

☐ **Who** the recount is about:

☐ **When** the events took place:

☐ **Where** the events took place:

☐ My recount tells the reader about one or more events in the correct order:

Writing review 2

✔

☐ I have used describing words to make my writing interesting.

Some describing words I have used:

☐ I have used different words to begin my sentences.

Some words I have used:

☐ My recount has a clear ending.

This is what I included in my ending: